In this story you will learn about the **short i** vowel sound. Can you find these words and sound them out?

will	**filled**	**milk**	**sip**
dish	**with**	**kittens**	

Here are some review sight words:

be   in   the   is   for   like

Here are some fun words:

what   woof   Biscuit   mew

What will be in the dish?

Mew!

The kittens like Biscuit.

Woof!

The dish is filled
with milk.

Is the milk for Biscuit?

Mew!

The milk is for the kittens.

Sip, sip.

Kittens like milk.